Yorkshire's Jurassic
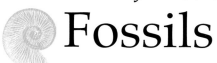 Fossils

Yorkshire's Jurassic Fossils
Published by High Tide Publishing, 2019
Copyright text Roger Osborne, 2019

Roger Osborne has asserted his right under the Copyright, Designs and
Patents Act, 1988 to be identified as the author of this work.

Copyright fossil images Whitby Museum

The author and publishers thank Whitby Museum for their kind
cooperation in the preparation of this book, and for permission to use
photographs of the museum's specimens. These images are copyright
and should not be used by any third party without express permission of
Whitby Museum.

All information and opinions expressed in this book are the responsibility
of the author and publisher.

A CIP catalogue record for this book is available from the British Library

ISBN 978-0-9933646-3-1

Designed by Wooden Ark, Woodend Workspace, Scarborough

Printed and bound in Great Britain by Adverset, Scarborough

To order copies of this and other High Tide publications visit
www.hightidepublishing.co.uk/shop

Retailers wishing to stock or restock any of our publications should email
hightidepublishing@btinternet.com

Yorkshire's Jurassic
Fossils

Roger Osborne

in association with

Contents

Yorkshire's Jurassic Fossils

Welcome to our pocket guide to the fossils of this beautiful coast. The Yorkshire coast is famous for its stunning landscapes and its amazing abundance of fossils. In this brief guide we will lead you through the main groups of fossils, show you good places to look for specimens, and give clues as to how to identify different fossil types.

This guide is illustrated with fossils from the amazing collection at Whitby Museum – one of the finest collections of Jurassic fossils anywhere. Make sure you visit this extraordinary museum during your visits to the coast. Full details at www.whitbymusuem.org.uk.

Fossils along the coast

The rocks of the Yorkshire coast contain a huge diversity of fossils. The Lower Jurassic rocks that stretch from Redcar to Robin Hood's Bay are famous for their marine fossils – ammonites, bivalves, belemnites and giant reptiles, as well as crustacea and gastropods. Middle Jurassic rocks sit on top of these and stretch from Runswick Bay south to Filey. These are mostly delta sediments containing plant fossils and dinosaur footprints. Upper Jurassic rocks run south of Scarborough to Filey; these are marine sediments containing corals, gastropods, ammonites and bivalves.

Identifying fossils

This guide gives some general advice about identification as well as lots of photos of fossils groups. To identify particular species you can try one of the sources listed on page 64.

Ancient worlds

The Yorkshire coast's rocks are from one of the most fascinating periods of earth history. The rocks become gradually younger from north to south so the coast acts as a slice through time – a journey from Redcar to Bridlington takes you through 130 million years of earth history. During this time the region went through a series of dramatic changes which have left us with an extraordinary range of rocks and fossils.

The Lower Jurassic rocks of the northern and central part of the coast were formed at the bottom of a sea and are packed with fossils of creatures like ammonites, bivalves, ichthyosaurs and plesiosaurs. Fossil plants and dinosaur footprints are common in Middle Jurassic rocks that sit on the tops of the cliffs. Then come the corals, sponges and ammonites of the Upper Jurassic around Scarborough and Filey. And finally there are echinoids and sponges and yet more ammonites in the Cretaceous chalk of Flamborough.

In addition there are trace fossils left by burrowing creatures, rarer finds like fossil fish and, from recent Pleistocene deposits, bones and teeth of ice age mammals.

All these fossils can be found in the rocks of the cliffs and scars of the coast. But huge quantities of fossils are also washed out of the cliffs, rolled around by the sea and deposited as pebbles on the beaches. In fact longshore drift carries fossils all the way down the coast, so you'll find Whitby ammonites as far south as Spurn Head. Pebble banks are therefore a great place to look for fossils so, in the middle of this book, we've provided a brief guide to beach fossils.

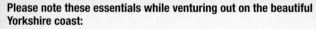

Please note these essentials while venturing out on the beautiful Yorkshire coast:

- **Check the tide times**
  It is easy to get cut off so time your outing with a falling tide.

- **Avoid the bottoms of cliffs**
  The cliffs here are dangerous with rocks continually falling from above.

- **Do not hack fossils out of rocks**
  There are Sites of Special Scientific Interest (SSSIs) all along the coast; it is illegal to disturb these. In any case loose fossils are easily found on the beaches and scars – it is generally all right to take small quantities of these for your personal use.

Ichthyosaurs

Giant fossil reptiles are among the glories of the Yorkshire coast. Ichthyosaurs are the most common marine reptile found here, usually as fragments but occasionally as whole skeletons. These dolphin-shaped creatures inhabited the seas through the whole Jurassic and into the Cretaceous Period – from 200 to 65 million years ago. They varied from 1 to 16 metres in length with most between 2 and 4 metres long.

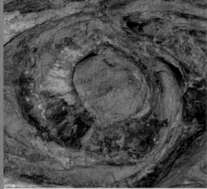

Ichthyosaurs had the largest eye of any known animal. One nine metre-long specimen had an eye 300mm across. This enabled the animals to see at depths of up to 600 metres.

Ichthyosaurs were reptiles, not fish. They breathed air and were probably warm-blooded. Their young were born underwater and had to swim immediately to the surface to take their first breath. Fossils containing as many as ten embryos have been found.

Whitby Museum has some spectacular reptile fossils built into its walls. This *Ichthyosaurus crassimanus* (now renamed *Temnodontosaurus*) is over seven metres long.

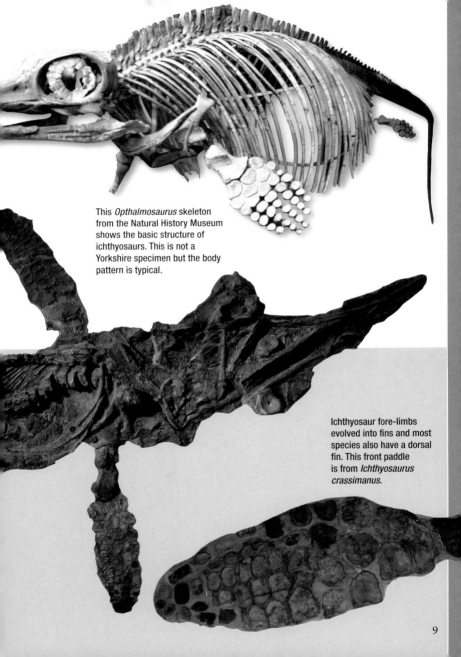

This *Opthalmosaurus* skeleton from the Natural History Museum shows the basic structure of ichthyosaurs. This is not a Yorkshire specimen but the body pattern is typical.

Ichthyosaur fore-limbs evolved into fins and most species also have a dorsal fin. This front paddle is from *Ichthyosaurus crassimanus*.

Ichthyosaur bones

While finds of whole ichthyosaur skeletons are rare, teeth, jaws and limb bones appear regularly. These are often washed out of the cliffs and end up on the shore. You are most likely to see them along the coast between Saltburn and Robin Hood's Bay. Reptile remains have been found in loose boulders of Alum Shale at Kettleness, Sandsend Ness and further south.

Reptile teeth become separated from the jaws and are often preserved separately within the matrix. When eroded out they can end up loose on beaches.

This close up of an ichthyosaur jaw shows how the individual cone-shaped teeth of the upper and lower jaws interlock.

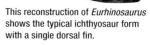

This reconstruction of *Eurhinosaurus* shows the typical ichthyosaur form with a single dorsal fin.

Jaws and teeth

Jaws and teeth are among the easiest ichthyosaur remains to recognise. The teeth are often grooved and found separately or in situ in jaws. The teeth can be eroded out of the jaws leaving impressions. Jaws and teeth preserve relatively well and are regularly found on the Yorkshire coast.

Vertebrae

Ichthyosaur vertebrae are preserved individually as shallow discs, with slightly concave surfaces. They are sometimes found still joined together in 'stacks'. Contrast the shallow discs with the deeper plesiosaur vertebrae and the 'cotton-reel' shapes of crocodile tail vertebrae.

Stacks of vertebrae like this are rare. This is an early specimen in the museum's collection.

Vertebrae from the thorax, or rib area, may have neural spines attached.

Bone fragments

Fragments of reptile bones occur in isolation or embedded in their background matrix. The ends of femurs, shoulder bones and ribs are all recognisable as reptile remains but some inorganic nodules also look like reptile parts, so you may need to cross-check against museum specimens.

Plesiosaurs

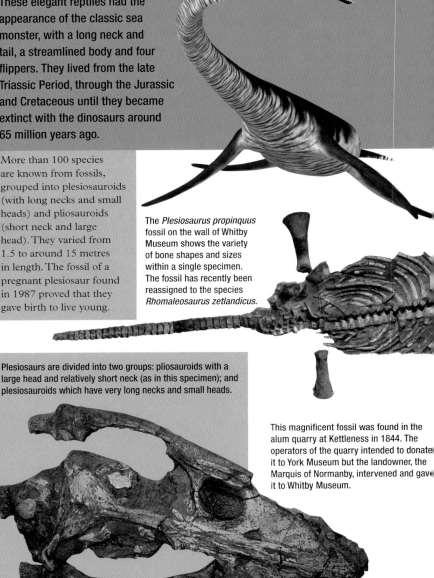

These elegant reptiles had the appearance of the classic sea monster, with a long neck and tail, a streamlined body and four flippers. They lived from the late Triassic Period, through the Jurassic and Cretaceous until they became extinct with the dinosaurs around 65 million years ago.

More than 100 species are known from fossils, grouped into plesiosauroids (with long necks and small heads) and pliosauroids (short neck and large head). They varied from 1.5 to around 15 metres in length. The fossil of a pregnant plesiosaur found in 1987 proved that they gave birth to live young.

The *Plesiosaurus propinquus* fossil on the wall of Whitby Museum shows the variety of bone shapes and sizes within a single specimen. The fossil has recently been reassigned to the species *Rhomaleosaurus zetlandicus*.

Plesiosaurs are divided into two groups: pliosauroids with a large head and relatively short neck (as in this specimen); and plesiosauroids which have very long necks and small heads.

This magnificent fossil was found in the alum quarry at Kettleness in 1844. The operators of the quarry intended to donate it to York Museum but the landowner, the Marquis of Normanby, intervened and gave it to Whitby Museum.

Rib cage

The central section of this specimen is virtually complete with a full rib cage and vertebrae.

The sharp curve of the ribs with a boomerang appearance is characteristic of the genus and species.

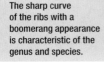

There are between 80 and 100 vertebrae in total in *Rhomaleosaurus zetlandicus*, with around 23 in the neck and 31 in the tail.

Substituting bones

It is likely that some of the bones in the paddle are from other specimens, which has made the task of identification complicated. This practice was commonplace in Victorian museums in order to enhance the display. Compare the bones in this paddle to the ichthyosaur fins.

Individual bones are often found embedded in nodules. These get eroded out of the cliffs and lie scattered on the beaches and scars of the coast.

A world of plesiosaurs

Plesiosaur fossils from the Whitby area have been exported across the world. Museums from Dublin to London and Harvard to Texas contain giant Whitby plesiosaurs in their collections. Most of the fossils were uncovered during quarrying for alum in the nineteenth century, and the soft Lower Jurassic Alum Shale is still the best source of reptile remains.

This reconstruction of a *Plesiosaurus dolochodeirus* skeleton shows the majestic form of these great reptiles.

Plesiosaurs were fast moving predators, living on ammonites and other molluscs but able to take on larger prey.

Coprolites

Coprolites – pieces of fossilised dung – give indications of animals' diets. This one, from the Whitby collection, contains tiny fragments of shells and is probably from a plesiosaur.

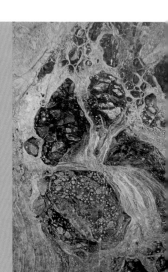

The large plesiosaur fossils from the Yorkshire coast were mostly recovered from the vast alum quarries dug along the coast from the 1600s to the 1870s.

Kettleness monster

The largest fossil ever discovered on the Yorkshire coast was a skeleton of *Rhomaleosaurus cramptoni*, found in the alum quarry at Kettleness in 1848. It measures over 7 by 4 metres and was donated by the Marquis of Normanby to his friend Philip Crampton. He took it to his home in Dublin and it now rests in the collection of the National Musuem of Ireland. This engraving is from the first description in 1863.

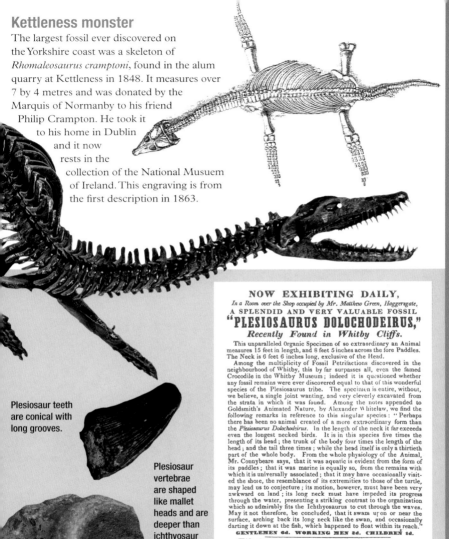

Plesiosaur teeth are conical with long grooves.

Plesiosaur vertebrae are shaped like mallet heads and are deeper than ichthyosaur vertebrae.

NOW EXHIBITING DAILY,

In a Room over the Shop occupied by Mr. Matthew Green, Haggersgate,

A SPLENDID AND VERY VALUABLE FOSSIL

"PLESIOSAURUS DOLOCHODEIRUS,"

Recently Found in Whitby Cliffs.

This unparalleled Organic Specimen of so extraordinary an Animal measures 15 feet in length, and 8 feet 5 inches across the fore Paddles. The Neck is 6 feet 6 inches long, exclusive of the Head.

Among the multiplicity of Fossil Petrifactions discovered in the neighbourhood of Whitby, this by far surpasses all, even the famed Crocodile in the Whitby Museum; indeed it is questioned whether any fossil remains were ever discovered equal to that of this wonderful species of the Plesiosaurus tribe. The specimen is entire, without, we believe, a single joint wanting, and very cleverly excavated from the strata in which it was found. Among the notes appended to Goldsmith's Animated Nature, by Alexander Whitelaw, we find the following remarks in reference to this singular species: "Perhaps there has been no animal created of a more extraordinary form than the *Plesiosaurus Dolochodeirus*. In the length of its neck it far exceeds even the longest necked birds. It is in this species five times the length of its head; the trunk of the body four times the length of the head; and the tail three times; while the head itself is only a thirtieth part of the whole body. From the whole physiology of the Animal, Mr. Connybeare says, that it was aquatic is evident from the form of its paddles; that it was marine is equally so, from the remains with which it is universally associated; that it may have occasionally visited the shore, the resemblance of its extremities to those of the turtle, may lead us to conjecture; its motion, however, must have been very awkward on land; its long neck must have impeded its progress through the water, presenting a striking contrast to the organization which so admirably fits the Ichthyosaurus to cut through the waves. May it not therefore, be concluded, that it swam upon or near the surface, arching back its long neck like the swan, and occasionally darting it down at the fish, which happened to float within its reach."

GENTLEMEN 6d. WORKING MEN 3d. CHILDREN 1d.

Whitby, August 7th, 1841.—HORNE AND RICHARDSON, PRINTERS, WHITBY.

A beautiful specimen of *Plesiosaurus dolichodeirus* was found in the alum shale at Robin Hood's Bay in 1841 by Matthew Green. The poster tells us that by August it was on display above a shop in Haggersgate before being bought by Cambridge University for £230. It is now in the Sedgwick Museum in Cambridge.

15

Crocodiles

The seas of the early Jurassic period were inhabited by marine crocodiles. The fossil remains of these teleosaurs have been found in Lower Jurassic Yorkshire rocks since the 1700s. Instead of paddles like the other marine reptiles, teleosaurs have legs and feet. They were similar to modern gharials which are found in northern India.

The finest fossil in Whitby Museum is *Teleosaurus chapmani*, found in 1824. It was discovered by a collector in 'the alum shale near Whitby'. This was just a year after the founding of the museum.

Partial remains of marine crocodiles, like these ribs and vertebrae, are found in the Lower Jurassic Alum Shale strata along the coast.

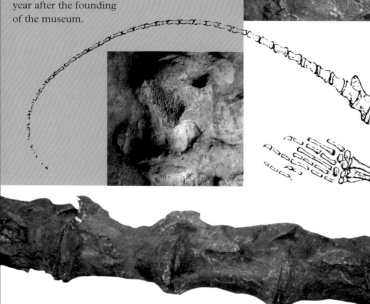

The long tail section of the teleosaur clearly shows the cotton-reel form of the individual vertebrae.

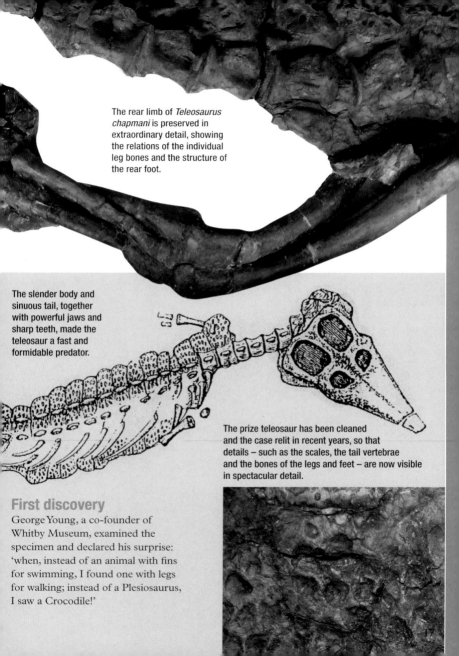

The rear limb of *Teleosaurus chapmani* is preserved in extraordinary detail, showing the relations of the individual leg bones and the structure of the rear foot.

The slender body and sinuous tail, together with powerful jaws and sharp teeth, made the teleosaur a fast and formidable predator.

The prize teleosaur has been cleaned and the case relit in recent years, so that details – such as the scales, the tail vertebrae and the bones of the legs and feet – are now visible in spectacular detail.

First discovery

George Young, a co-founder of Whitby Museum, examined the specimen and declared his surprise: 'when, instead of an animal with fins for swimming, I found one with legs for walking; instead of a Plesiosaurus, I saw a Crocodile!'

Dinosaur footprints

Dinosaurs were here during Middle Jurassic times when the Yorkshire coast was a coastal plain, with multiple streams running through mud and sandbanks. Tree-ferns, cycads, horse-tails and ginkgoes grew along the river banks providing food for a variety of creatures. The legacy of this ancient environment includes a huge variety of plant fossils along with thousands of preserved dinosaur tracks, making it a site of global importance.

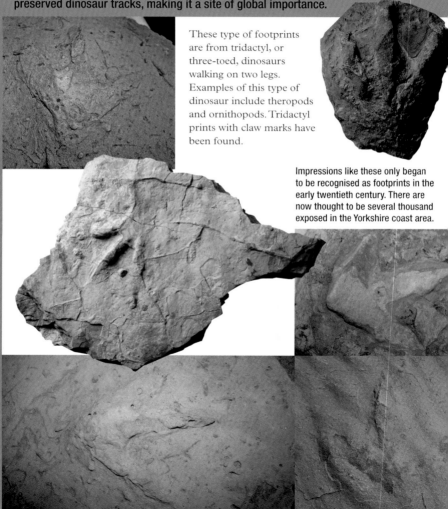

These type of footprints are from tridactyl, or three-toed, dinosaurs walking on two legs. Examples of this type of dinosaur include theropods and ornithopods. Tridactyl prints with claw marks have been found.

Impressions like these only began to be recognised as footprints in the early twentieth century. There are now thought to be several thousand exposed in the Yorkshire coast area.

These footprints near Scarborough are seen in section. Notice how the layers of substrate have been bent downwards by the gradual force; the round piece of rock above has been dislodged from the upper layers of sandy mud by the dinosaur foot.

Size and behaviour

Tracks give a lot of information about their makers including height from foot to hip and from hip to shoulder, the type of gait and the speed of movement. We can also learn about their abundance, diversity and whether they lived in groups. Tracks tell us about possible migration paths, preferred habitats and the state of the ground beneath their feet. Animals' feet push down into a soft material like sand or mud. The impression gets filled, preserving the print. What you see depends on how the rock is exposed. Tracks on scars tend to be impressions, tracks on fallen blocks are often seen from underneath, so the print stands out in the form of the infill.

Rounded footprints like these were made by four-legged dinosaurs such as sauropods and stegosaurids. A trackway of twelve sauropod prints has been found at Scalby Bay near Scarborough.

Where to see footprints

Dinosaur tracks have been found throughout the Ravenscar Group of Middle Jurassic strata. Locations include Port Mulgrave, Saltwick to Hawsker, Hayburn Wyke to Scalby Bay, and Cornelian Bay to Cayton Bay. Tracks are sometimes in the scar, but mostly in slabs fallen from the cliffs. They are generally difficult to spot; so go on an organised walk to see them. If you do find tracks don't disturb them or try to chip them out. Take photographs, note the location and contact Whitby Museum.

19

Ammonites

The coiled shells of ammonites make the most beautiful and distinctive fossils. The fossils are quite common on the Yorkshire coast, particularly in Lower Jurassic rocks. As well as being easy to recognise, ammonites are of great scientific importance. They are used to plot time zones within the Jurassic; geologists worked out how to subdivide and correlate rocks by changes in fossil types on this coast. Ammonites first evolved around 200 million years ago and died out 65 million years ago at the same time as the dinosaurs.

Exotic squid

Ammonites were molluscs, a group that includes present-day squid and snails. The animal lived in the outermost chamber of multi-chambered coiled shells that floated freely. They were able to adjust their depth by changing the amount of gas in the chambers of their shell. They could move rapidly by squirting water outwards.

This ammonite fossil has been cut in half and polished, showing the beautifully preserved internal chambers.

Siphuncle
Chambers (Septa)
Suture line
Mantle
Beak
Funnel (Hypernome)
Stomach
Gills

Ammonite chambers were linked by a tube, called a siphuncle, which was used to adjust the depth at which the ammonite was swimming. The tentacles drew in plankton for food.

Sutures

The outlines of the chamber walls or septa are sometimes preserved on the outer surface of fossils. These suture lines are complex and highly distinctive. This *Hildoceras bifrons* is either worn or is an internal cast revealing the suture marks.

Common in Yorkshire

The most common group or 'genus' of ammonites is *Dactylioceras* followed by *Hildoceras*. Other common genera include *Harpoceras*, *Phylloceras*, *Eleganticeras* and *Pseudolioceras*. There are at least 40 genera found on the Yorkshire coast.

Hildoceras

Dactylioceras

Eleganticeras

Harpoceras

Pseudolioceras

Phylloceras

These are six common genera of ammonite on the Yorkshire coast. To tell the difference check the ribs, keel and whether they are involute or evolute.

Involute and evolute

Ammonites come in lots of sizes but all share a basic coiled structure. But there are two types of coils and these can help you tell one genus from another. In evolute ammonites the outer chambers lie outside the inner chambers so that there is an obvious coiling effect. Involute ammonites have the outer chambers overlapping the inner chambers so the fossil looks more like a plate than a coil.

Evolute

Involute

Caloceras

Cleviceras

Caloceras shows the classic visible coils of an evolute ammonite. Cleviceras ammonites are involute with the outer whorl covering the inner whorls.

Ammonite diversity

Finding any ammonite fossil is a treat for most visitors to the Yorkshire coast. But as you get to see more ammonites you begin to appreciate their huge diversity. It is this diversity that makes ammonites so valuable as scientific specimens. Rapid evolution and wide distribution gives ammonites a key role in understanding the Jurassic environment and how the rock strata relate to each other.

Nodules

Hard nodules have formed within different Jurasic rocks along the coast. The nodules are created during the process of hardening, when the soft sediments are being squeezed under pressure. Minerals within the sediments migrate and often coalesce around objects like shells. This is why nodules occasionally contain fossils like this *Dactylioceras commune*.

Look carefully at nodules to see if parts of ammonite keels are showing. Any nodule containing an ammonite is likely to be a flattened sphere, probably with a seam or crack around the rim. The most common ammonites found on the coast are species of the *Dactylioceras* genus.

This nodule contains a spectacular collection of ammonite fossils. Note the sickle-shaped ribs that indicate these are probably *Eleganticeras elegantulum*. This half of the nodule contains both fossils and impressions.

Type fossils

Whitby Museum has around 150 ammonite holotypes in its collection. These are the standard specimens by which each species of ammonite is defined, and are therefore of unique scientific importance. Most were collected and catalogued in the 19th century by Martin Simpson, the curator at the museum. These are just a few examples.

1. *Paltopleuroceras birdi*
2. *Phridoceras quadricornutum*
3. *Phridoceras armatum*
4. *Euagiceras transformatum*
5. *Amaltheus reticularis*
6. *Paltopleuroceras elaboratum*

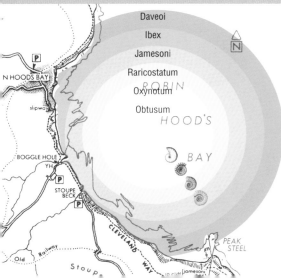

Zone fossils

Short-lived species and a widespread free-floating habit make ammonites excellent as zone fossils. The Jurassic is divided into ammonite zones. At Robin Hood's Bay the erosion of a dome-shaped structure gives a number of consecutive zones spread across the scar; the zones are shown roughly on this sketch map.

Identifying ammonites

Ammonites might look similar to each other but there are some useful ways to tell the different species apart. Once you've decided whether the one you've found is evolute or involute (see page 19) then have a good look at the ribs. Some common ammonite groups, like *Dactylioceras* and *Phylloceras*, have straight ribs. Other groups have ribs with a simple curve, such as *Hildoceras bifrons*, while in others the curves are more complex. In some species the ribs are fine; in others they are heavy. Finally, some ammonite groups (eg *Stephanoceras*) have ribs that divide or bifurcate.

Dactylioceras tenuicostatum

Hildoceras bifrons

Peronoceras fibulatum

Harpoceras serpentinum

Hildiates murleyi

Quenstedoeras lamberti

Pleuroceras hawskerense

Dactylioceras commune

Lytoceras fimbriatum

Eoderoceras armatus

Hildoceras levinsoni

Keels

The edge of an ammonite is known as the keel or venter. In some groups, eg *Dactylioceras*, the ribs run across the keel without interruption. In others, like *Paltopleuroceras* there is a single keel; other genera have double or knotted keels.

Left to right:
Pleuroceras sp.
Amauroceras ferrugineum
Peronoceras turriculatum
Hildaites murleyi
Paltopleuroceras sp.
Schlotheimia redcarensis
Hildoceras bifrons

Upper Jurassic

Almost all the ammonite fossils found on the Yorkshire coast are from Lower Jurassic rocks. But occasionally Middle and Upper Jurassic ammonites like *Goweiceras* and *Tornquistes* crop up, mainly south of Scarborough. Note the pale cream and sand colour of these rocks compared with the lower Jurassic shales.

Nautiloids

Nautiloids, like ammonites and belemnites, are cephalopods. The nautiloids have survived to the present day and are found in deep waters off Asia and Australia. Fossil nautiloids are known from the late Cambrian onwards and are thought to be the original group that gave rise to the ammonites and belemnites. Jurassic nautiloid fossils are not as common as ammonites on the Yorkshire coast but there are several in Whitby Museum's collection.

Nautilus pompilius

The modern nautilus is a free-floating carnivore living mainly off crustaceans. It draws animals into its hard jaws using an array of tentacles. The shell markings reflect the walls of the internal chambers. In nautiloids these are simple curves, whereas ammonites have much more complex septa.

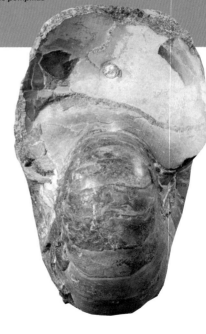

Cenoceras astacoides is a massive nautiloid fossil from the Whitby collection. The tapering out of the shell provides a large body chamber in which the animal lived. This is from the Upper Lias strata of the Lower Jurassic.

Internal structure

This section through a modern nautilus shell shows the multiple chambers with simple curved septa separating the chambers. The animal is perfectly buoyant, adjusting its depth through a siphuncle or tube which connects the gas-filled chambers. They move by pumping water outwards in a form of jet propulsion.

Modern nautiloids live in deep water, generally over 100 metres deep, with some living 700 metres down. They are found mainly in the Indian and southwest Pacific Oceans.

This magnificent *Cenoceras annularis* clearly shows the suture lines that reflect the septa, or chamber walls, within. Also from the upper part of the Lower Jurassic.

Bivalves

On the Yorkshire coast bivalves are everywhere. When you stroll across the scar or clamber over banks of pebbles there's a good chance you'll be walking on fossil bivalves. And when you look in rock pools or intertidal zones you'll find live bivalves everywhere too. Cockles, mussels, oysters, clams and scallops all belong to this diverse and long-lived group. Their variety makes them fascinating and scientifically important.

What are bivalves?

Every bivalve has two shells or valves which can be opened by the animal inside. In most cases, for example mussels and scallops, the two shells are almost identical. But in other groups, like the genus *Gryphaea*, the shells are different.

The profusion of living bivalves, and their importance as food for humans, means that many groups have common names such as oysters, mussels, cockles and scallops. Fossils can be referred to by these common names or by names such as pinna or pecten.

Clusters of *Meleagrinella* [above] and *Myophorella* [below] show fossils standing out from their background matrix.

Fossil bivalve shells like these pectens are often found grouped together. This can be because they live like this or because the shells are washed together by currents.

ow do they live?

valves have existed since the
ambrian period, 500 million
ars ago. Unlike the ammonites
d belemnites, bivalves are
ainly sedentary, attaching
emselves to rocks or – like
zor clams – burrowing into sand.
ey use muscles and ligaments to
en and close their shells taking in
icroscopic phytoplankton and oxygen
rough gills.
me bivalves can swim short distances by
pping their shells together, and a cockle
n even flex its foot in order to jump.

Ceratomya petricosa

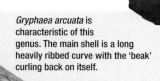

Gryphaea arcuata is
characteristic of this
genus. The main shell is a long
heavily ribbed curve with the 'beak'
curling back on itself.

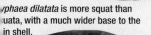

yphaea dilatata is more squat than
uata, with a much wider base to the
in shell.

Gryphaea

Gryphaea is a genus of the order
Ostreoida or oysters. Unlike most
bivalves the two shells, or valves, are
quite different. One is curved and
bulbous, while the other acts as a lid. In
Gryphaea the curve of the larger valve
is highly distinctive, sometimes curling
back on itself. This curve gives the genus
the common name Devil's Toenail.
The animal lived inside the two valves.
Opening the valves allowed nutrient-rich
waters to flow in.

29

Bivalve diversity

The latest attempt at scientific classification recognised 324 bivalve families with more than 9,000 living species in over 1,000 genera! Thankfully, fossils from the Yorkshire coast come from just a few families and are generally easy to recognise. The best indications are shape, size and markings. The *Pinna* genus has the largest specimens from this area; the long slender shells can reach up to 90 cm. The smallest are just a few millimeters in size. The most common fossil bivalves found on the Yorkshire coast are pectens, trigoniids, inoceramids, oysters, cardiniids, oxytomids, pholadomyids, hiatelloids and nuculoids.

1

Shape variety

Bivalves show a huge variety of shapes and sizes. The shell shape of some species reflects their need to burrow into sand and mud to escape predators. Others anchor themselves to rocks, or sit on the seafloor. These specimens give an idea of the variety of bivalve shapes.

2

1 *Pinna folium*
2 *Cardinia* sp.
3 *Inoceramid*
4 *Plagiostoma gigantea*

3

4

1 Arcomya longissima
2 Arcomya concinna
3 Entolium lunare
4 Dacromya ovum

1 Pseudopecten equivalvis
2 Trigonia costata
3 Gresslya intermedia
4 Pholadomya ambigua
5 Inoperna scalprum

31

Bivalve hinges and ribs

The arrangement of hinges and the characteristics of the growth lines and ribs are good indicators of bivalve genus and species. The two shells of the bivalve are joined at the hinge by a ligament. The shells often protrude above this ligament in a hump known as the umbo. Contraction of adductor muscles closes the valves, relaxation of the muscles allows them to open. The gills of bivalves have evolved into organs that combine breathing and feeding.

Evolutionary changes

Bivalves are distinguished by the ways in which the shells are layered and by differing arrangement of hinges, teeth and musculature. All these have altered over the long evolutionary life of bivalves.

The umbones in *Gresslya peregrina*, above, almost curve over the hinge area.

It is rare to find both valves of a bivalve preserved in an open state as in this *Cardinia hybrida*.

Note the patterns of ribs and growth lines around the hinge in this *Pholadomya murchisoni*.

Bivalve ribs and spines

Bivalves generally have growth lines showing as rings circling outwards from the umbo. Some species have ribs that radiate from the umbo. Inoceramids have moderate to strong growth lines, whereas pectens have strong radial ornament.

Some bivalve species have spines, though these are rarely preserved as perfectly as on this *Palmoxytoma cygnipes*.

1. *Inoceramus*
2. *Gryphaea cymbium*
3. *Psuedopecten equivalvis* [impression]
4. *Gresslya intermedia*
5. *Spondylus spinosus* [Cretaceous fossil; note the remains of spines]

Beach fossils

Fossils are abundant all along the Yorkshire coast but it's easy to miss the most obvious ones. While books and museums are full of pictures of perfect specimens, most fossils on the coast are in pieces, or embedded in rocks, or appear only as outline markings. The good news is that once you know what you're looking for, you'll find that the beaches are full of beautiful, if imperfect, specimens.

Head to nearest bank of pebbles on an open beach and start turning over the stones. Fossils are generally in the pale grey shale, yellow sandstone or reddish ironstone pebbles. This collection shows only the most common types of local fossil found in beach pebbles, including ammonites, bivalves and belemnites.

This flat pebble looked innocuous on the beach. But looking through a hand lens reveals small bivalves and gastropods packed together.

Ammonites commonly occur as broken curved sections of outer whorls. Whole ammonites are embedded in nodules or found as imprints, sometimes worn to just a faint impression. Most of these ammonite fragments are *Dactylioceras commune*, the commonest Yorkshire coast ammonite.

This close up of a beach pebble shows a cluster of Carboniferous rugose corals probably from the Pennines.

Pebble variety

Jurassic fossils like these ammonites, bivalves, belemnites and gastropods are plentiful on the beaches of the Yorkshire coast. In addition there are fossils and rocks from distant places, brought here by ice sheets from Scotland, Scandinavia, the Lake District and the Pennines.

Longshore drift fetches Lower Jurassic fossils from Redcar and Whitby down the coast all the way to Spurn Point and beyond.

Cayton Bay (above), Sandsend (left) and Scarborough (below) are among the places you will find fossils. But just look anywhere where there are pebbles.

Scar fossils

Many of the beaches on this coast have beautiful wave-cut platforms or scars. These flat areas of rock have been worn smooth by countless tides washing in over the even layers of Jurassic rock. Fossils are exposed on the surface of the scar, sometimes just the odd specimen, but sometimes by the thousand. If you see fossils in the scar, please enjoy them and leave them to be appreciated by others.

The scar at Saltwick is embedded with lots of belemnites and ammonites. This is a SSSI. It is illegal to disturb the bed rock so pick up loose specimens rather than hacking at the scar.

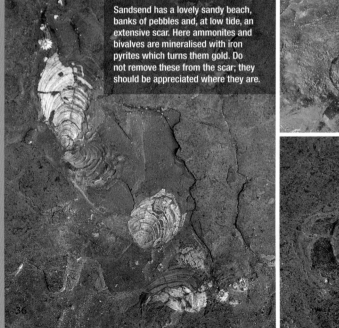

Sandsend has a lovely sandy beach, banks of pebbles and, at low tide, an extensive scar. Here ammonites and bivalves are mineralised with iron pyrites which turns them gold. Do not remove these from the scar; they should be appreciated where they are.

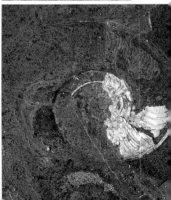

The scar at Staithes has lots of individual fossils. This belemnite reveals its internal structure. A stratum known as the Oyster Bed is exposed here, showing thousands of bivalves packed together; tiny winkles have inhabited the dips in the scar.

There are huge expanses of scar at Saltburn, Robin Hood's Bay and along most of the Yorkshire coast.

Belemnites

One of the most common fossil groups on the Yorkshire coast, belemnites are found everywhere from Saltburn in the north to Speeton in the south. Either embedded in rock or lying loose on the beach, their distinctive bullet shape marks them out. While they all look similar to the untrained eye, it takes only a little guidance to begin to recognise the different genera.

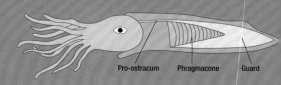

Pro-ostracum   Phragmacone   Guard

Belemnite fossils are the remains of squid-like creatures. They became extinct at the end of the Cretaceous Period. Within each body was a guard or rostrum to balance against the heavy head. The animal was anchored in a conical phragmacone at the front of the guard and a thin protrusion or pro-ostracum is sometimes preserved.

Hibolites jaculum

Acrcoelites (Odontobelus) vulgaris

Youngibelus simpsoni

Parapassaloteuthis robusta

Acrocoelites toarcibelus

Sepia cuspidata

Different belemnite genera and species are distinguished by shape and by grooves running down the guard. Most common shapes are cylindrical, conical and hastate – shaped like an old-fashioned vase. Some species have flattened or extended ends and others show a different shape when viewed laterally or ventrally. These are some examples of the huge variety of Jurassic belemnites in Yorkshire.

Youngibelus tubularis

Hastites spadixari

Pseudohastites scabrous

Acrocelites (Odontobelus) pyramidalis

Passaloteuthis bisulcata

Brachiopods

Though similar in appearance to bivalves, brachiopods are a distinct and very common group of shellfish. One of the longest lived animal groups, brachiopods are abundant both in life and in the fossil record. They are also very diverse with over 5,000 genera and 12,000 fossil species. Most of the species living today are found in deep water. Several distinct fossil orders and genera are present on the Yorkshire coast, fairly easily distinguished by the shapes of the fossil shells.

In life

Brachiopods have two shells which they open for feeding and then close for protection. The two main groups – articulate and inarticulate – use muscles in different ways to open and close their shells. They live only in seawater. One shell (the pedicle valve) has a hole for a stalk, or pedicle, which anchors the animal to the seabed while keeping it clear of sediment. The other shell is the brachial valve. Brachiopods thrive in quiet conditions away from turbulent waves and tides.

Rhynchonellids have heavy ribs and a characteristic fold in the lower edge. They are the most common living brachiopod and are common all along the Yorkshire coast. This group is from the Whitby Museum collection. Like most seashell fossils they are occasionally found in clusters within nodules.

Fossil recognition

The easiest way to recognize brachiopods is through the shape of the shells. Fossils of lingula are found in some Lower Jurassic shales, though some are only 2mm in length. Spiriferid specimens occur in Redcar Mudstone at Huntcliff. Much more common are terebratulids and rhynchonellids.

Terebratulids from the Dogger formation are quite round and bulbous. There are no ribs. Some terebratulids have a straighter edge at the bottom.

Spiriferid fossils usually have a straight edge along the top and are often wider than they are deep. In ancient China they were called 'stone swallows' because of their resemblance to birds.

Brachiopods and other fossil shells are common among the pebbles and in the cliffs in places like Saltburn and Skinningrove, and all the way south to Filey Bay.

Gastropods

Easily recognisable from their spiral shape, gastropod fossils are found in many of the rocks of the Yorkshire coast. They are the most diverse class of all the molluscs with over 600 families still living in almost every habitat on earth. Marine gastropod fossils occur throughout most of the Jurassic and Cretaceous and are common in parts of the Upper Jurassic Coralline Oolite Formation.

Gastropods in life

Gastropod literally means 'stomach foot' and the large foot is the most visible part of the animal. The adaptability of this foot has allowed gastropods to live in deep oceans, high mountains and deserts. Marine gastropods have developed gills; some live on seaweed, others burrow into sand and use a siphon to draw in water. While many gastropods develop a snail-like shell some, such as limpets, have a conical shell – and slugs have no shell at all.

❶ *Bourgetia saemanni*
❷ *Pleurotomaria*
❸ *Pleurotomaria*
❹ *Aptyxiella* sp

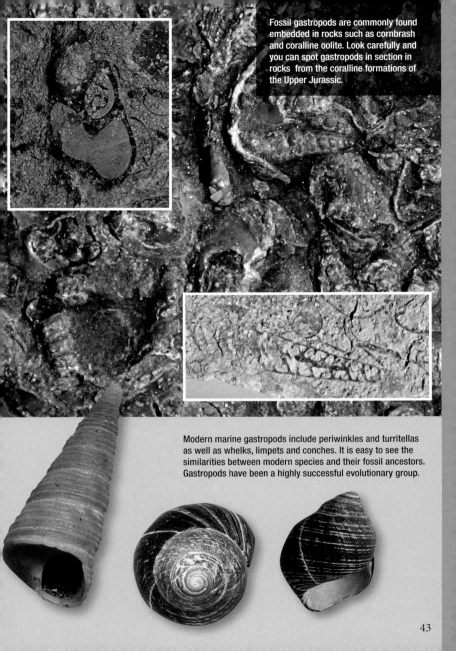

Fossil gastropods are commonly found embedded in rocks such as cornbrash and coralline oolite. Look carefully and you can spot gastropods in section in rocks from the coralline formations of the Upper Jurassic.

Modern marine gastropods include periwinkles and turritellas as well as whelks, limpets and conches. It is easy to see the similarities between modern species and their fossil ancestors. Gastropods have been a highly successful evolutionary group.

Echinoderms

This diverse group contains some of the most beautiful marine animals including echinoids (commonly called sea urchins), crinoids (sea lilies) and stelleroids (starfish). Although they look quite different from each other all these animals have a striking five-point symmetry inherited from a common ancestor. In life they develop a particular type of flexible skeleton and these are commonly preserved as fossils from the Cambrian period onwards.

Echinoids

Sea urchins are common across the world. They live in shallow rockpools and at depths of up to 5,000 metres. Fossil echinoids are common from the Cambrian Period 500 million years ago to the present. They are reasonably common along the Yorkshire coast, particularly in Upper Jurassic and Cretaceous rocks of the southern part.

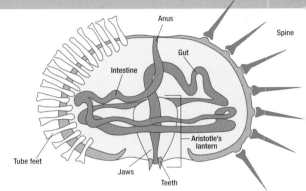

This section through a typical echinoderm shows the mouth at the bottom with the anus at the top, connected by a long digestive tract. The Aristotle's lantern is a jaw-like structure that scrapes nutrients off the surface and towards the mouth.

The echinoid fossil *Paracidaris florigemma* has a strikingly different shape from most other species. This one is from the Upper Jurassic Coralline Oolite Formation.

Echinoid fossils

These beautiful fossils typically have the appearance of a slightly squashed sphere with lots of variations in size and shape. The five part symmetry of echinoids can be hard to spot in modern shells; in fossils it is more obvious. Often the plates that make up the shell are worn smooth, leaving just five double grooves to identify the fossil as an echinoid.

This Whitby museum specimen of *Procidaris edwardsii* shows the original spines.

Though spheroid in shape, echinoid fossils vary from heart-shaped to squashed spheres. Heart-shaped micrasters are commonly found in Cretaceous chalk.

Crinoids

Crinoids are close relatives of the echinoids and part of the echinoderm family. All these animals are still thriving in today's seas and all are found as fossils in the rocks of the Yorkshire coast. The echinoderm family was particularly suited to conditions in the early and late Jurassic and in parts of the Cretaceous, so this is where we most commonly find their fossils.

Sea lilies

Though they look similar to plants, crinoids are animals. They attach themselves to rock and have a single stem with multiple branches that culminate in a head or calyx. The tentacles draw food in to a central mouth. Some species become free-floating as they mature.

Hispidocrinus scalaris

The stems of crinoids are made up of segments known as ossicles stacked on top of each other. The segments are often shaped like five-pointed stars or pentagons. The stems frequently break up after death and their fossilised remains are found scattered through local rocks.

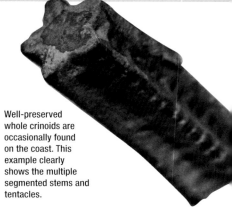

Well-preserved whole crinoids are occasionally found on the coast. This example clearly shows the multiple segmented stems and tentacles.

Crinoid stem segments are either hollow circles, like polo mints, or pentagon shapes, reflecting the five-sided symmetry of the echinoderm family. They are common in pebbles all along the coast.

Eocomatula interbrachiatus

In crinoids tentacles surround the mouth, drawing food in. The ten tentacles follow the five-point symmetry of the echinoderm family.

A slab of multiple *Pentacrinites subnotomous* crinoids is on display in Whitby Museum. The fine-grained shale has preserved the fine detail of the crinoids in exquisite detail. The largest fossil ever found has a stem 40 metres in length.

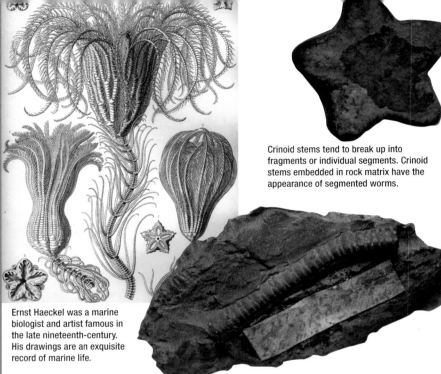

Crinoid stems tend to break up into fragments or individual segments. Crinoid stems embedded in rock matrix have the appearance of segmented worms.

Ernst Haeckel was a marine biologist and artist famous in the late nineteenth-century. His drawings are an exquisite record of marine life.

Structure

The echinoderms are zoologically separate from all other groups. They are exclusively marine and contain a complex internal system of tubes and vessels that transport fluid. These are connected to external tube feet, which are used for movement, respiration and feeding. Their skeletons are made of calcite and are easily preserved, making crinoids, in particular, abundant in the fossil record. Crinoidal limestones from the Carboniferous Period are largely made up of the stems of crinoids.

Starfish

Starfish is the common name for two kinds of echinoderms that occur in Jurassic sediments. The overall class is *Stelleroidea*; the first subclass is *Asteroidea*, which are the starfish proper; the second subclass is *Ophiuroidea*, commonly known as brittle stars. The five limbs present in both groups reflect the same five-fold symmetry found in echinoids and crinoids.

Stelleroidea have five limbs following the pattern of all echinoderms.

Brittle stars and starfish

While starfish and brittle stars are common, complete fossils are rare – the flexible skeleton tends to disintegrate – but some examples have been found on the Yorkshire coast. In asteroids the five limbs are continual from the central disk, whereas in ophiuroids there is a definite break between the centre and the limbs.

Complete starfish and brittle star fossils are rare finds on the Yorkshire coast.

Crustacea

Familiar creatures such as crabs, lobsters, shrimps, krill and crayfish all belong to the crustacean group. All crustacea have an exoskeleton which they regularly shed in order to grow. The exoskeleton is relatively thin and crustacea fossils are often delicate and fragile. They are rarer finds than hard-shelled creatures like ammonites and bivalves.

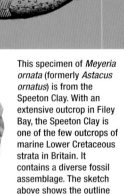

This specimen of *Meyeria ornata* (formerly *Astacus ornatus*) is from the Speeton Clay. With an extensive outcrop in Filey Bay, the Speeton Clay is one of the few outcrops of marine Lower Cretaceous strata in Britain. It contains a diverse fossil assemblage. The sketch above shows the outline more clearly.

Structure

The body of most crustacea is divided into segments known as somites. The head segment has antennae, mouthparts and jaws; the thorax segments each have a pair of legs and the abdomen has swimming legs, the anus and often a pair of appendages forming a tail fan.

Glyphaea lyrica shows the exoskeleton segments of the thorax. This is often the most visible part of any fossil crustacean. The legs and other appendages are often destroyed or mangled during preservation.

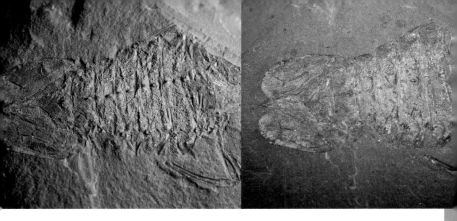

This rock has been split open to reveal the abdomen of a Jurassic lobster. The segments of the exoskeleton are clear together with the tail fan. Antennae are also visible.

The best-preserved crustacean in the Whitby collection, this fossil is from the *Eryma* genus. While lobster-like creatures have a similar body plan they are extremely diverse within limits. Note the massive claws together with head and thorax.

Fish

Fossil fish are found in the Lower Jurassic strata of the Yorkshire coast. Complete specimens are rare but scales, fins and teeth are much more common and definitely worth looking out for. Fish emerged during the early Palaeozoic Era, more than 500 million years ago. Preservation of fish is more difficult than shells or bones, and the fossils are often delicate, but significant finds have been made in this region.

Lepidotus semiserratus

These two specimens in Whitby Museum are from the *Lepidotes* genus. Up to 30 cm long, lepidotes were covered in enamelled scales. Their powerful teeth were used to crush mollusc shells.

This beautifully preserved *Pholidophorus bechei* is around 15 cm long. It was found at Saltwick near Whitby. Fish of the genus *Pholidophorus* were fast swimming predators with cartilaginous skeletons.

The *Caturus* genus were salmon-like fish with the sharp teeth of a marine predator. This beautiful fish head in Whitby Museum has been identified as *Caturus* but ID remains uncertain.

Fish scales like these show up in Lower Jurassic shales, both in situ and in larger beach pebbles.

Sharks shed their teeth regularly throughout their lives, so shark's teeth are common. There is great variety of shapes and sizes among sharks' and fishes' teeth. Compare them to the reptile teeth on page 10.

Plants

In the Middle Jurassic period the Yorkshire coast was a coastal plain. Freshwater streams ran through forests and undergrowth containing a rich variety of plant life. A variety of vegetation has been preserved and the rocks of the coast are famous for their plant fossils. While not as easily preserved as marine shells, exquisite plant fossils can be found in many Middle Jurassic rocks.

Ginkgos

Ginkgos are an ancient plant group characterized by fan-shaped leaves. The sole survivor of the group is *Ginkgo biloba*, the maidenhair tree. In the Jurassic period ginkgos were much more diverse and abundant.

The fan-shaped leaves are clearly visible in these ginkgo specimens from Whitby Museum, *Ginkgo digitata* [above] and *Baiera gracilis* [left]. The top specimen shows ginkgo leaves scattered across the substrate. All these are from Middle Jurassic strata.

Ptilophyllum sp.

This beautiful flower-like fossil is *Weltrichia spectabilis*, now recognized as the seed head of *Otozamites parallelus*.

Otozamites acuminatus

Bennettitales

The Bennettitales are a group of plants that flourished during the Jurassic but became extinct in the Cretaceous. They are distinguished from cycads by certain detailed features of their leaves.

Their spectacular seed-heads look similar to flowers and this group was once thought to be the direct ancestors of angiosperms or flowering plants, but this is no longer thought likely.

Taeneopteris major

Otozamites parallelus

Jurassic jungle

Plant fossils from this area tell us that there was a wide variety of vegetation. Flowering plants had not yet evolved and a wide range of ferns, conifers, ginkgos and araucarias thrived. Many Jurassic plants are still in existence. You can see tree ferns, ginkgos and conifers in the Jurassic garden in Pannett Park, Whitby – just near Whitby Museum.

Conifers

Cone-bearing trees and bushes were common in the Jurassic. These were broadly similar to their present-day descendants. Their remains are preserved in Middle Jurassic rocks but also in the Lower Jurassic deposits as the mineral jet.

Some trees were washed into the sea during the early Jurassic and preserved in the seafloor sediments as jet. Jet is different from other fossilised wood as it is impregnated with bitumen. Jet was long thought to be derived exclusively from trees of the araucaria family but this is now in doubt.

Jet is found in a particular set of strata (known as the Jet Rock) within the Whitby Mudstone.

Brachyphyllum (right) is an extinct member of the araucaria family and is a close relative of the Monkey Puzzle.

Equisetum beanii

Horsetails

The long straight stems of _Equisetum columnare_ are common in Middle Jurassic strata along the coast.

Equisetum columnare

Ctenis falcata

Cycads

Cycads now grow mainly in dry tropical areas and are less diverse than in the Jurassic period. They have stems covered in scale leaves with a tuft of leaves sticking out at the top.

Nilssonia compta

Identifying plants

Plant fossils are generally quite recognisable as leaves or stems but further identification is a complex process needing specialist help. Classification depends on intricate details of leaf arrangement and vein patterns. Different parts of plants can be preserved separately and carry different names; eg one name each for the leaves, stem, and reproductive parts. Plant fossils provide crucial information about Jurassic environments.

Neuropteris undulata

Ferns

Ferns (properly known as pteridophytes) are familiar to us today. Fossil ferns belong to groups that are still living, some dating as far back as the great Carboniferous coal forests. The main distinction within fern fossils is between fertile ferns, such as todites, and sterile ferns such as cladophlebis and coniopteris. So-called tree ferns are also true ferns, and include members of the *Dicksoniaceae* family. The seed ferns or pteridosperms are a separate group and are now extinct. They are characterized by thick leathery leaves on each side of a central axis.

Kylikipteris arguta is a tree fern and member of the *Dicksoniaceae* family.

The fern family presents some of the most striking fossil plants in the Middle Jurassic sediments of the Yorkshire coast.
Clathopteris whitbiensis [left]; *Coniopteris hymenophylloides* [below]; *Laccopteris polypodioides* [bottom left]; *Cladophlebis denticulata* [bottom right].

Trace fossils

Animals leave lots of traces in the landscape. Only some of these are preserved as fossils but these remains are precious indicators of ancient environments. The best-known trace fossils on the Yorkshire coast are footprints left by dinosaurs [see page 18]. But the most common remains are burrows left in mud, sand and rock by a variety of creatures. Look carefully and you will find these in abundance on almost every part of the coast.

Thalassinoides

Thick patterns of tubes that stand out on the surface of rocks are usually the remains of thalassinoides burrows. The burrows are made by small crustaceans in muddy seafloors. As the mud is buried and hardened into rock they get infilled with harder material; this stands out when the rock is eroded by the sea. Thalassinoides fossils show up as networks of tubes on rock surfaces. The outcrop of Hambleton Oolite at Filey Brigg is rich in thalassinoides burrows. You can spot them on fallen rocks all along the coast at places like Cayton Bay.

The outcrop of Hambleton Oolite at Filey Brigg is rich in thalassinoides burrows.

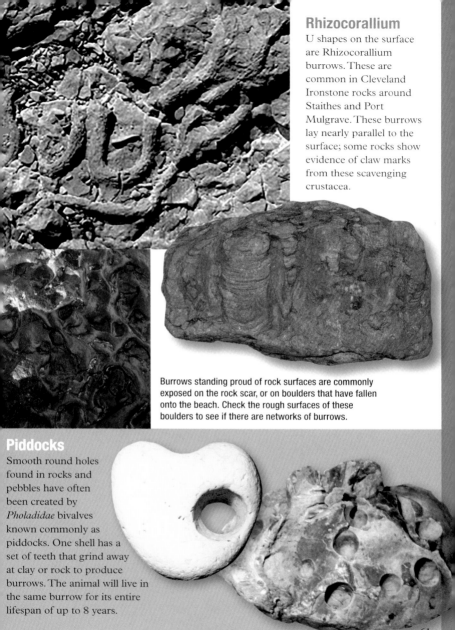

Rhizocorallium

U shapes on the surface are Rhizocorallium burrows. These are common in Cleveland Ironstone rocks around Staithes and Port Mulgrave. These burrows lay nearly parallel to the surface; some rocks show evidence of claw marks from these scavenging crustacea.

Burrows standing proud of rock surfaces are commonly exposed on the rock scar, or on boulders that have fallen onto the beach. Check the rough surfaces of these boulders to see if there are networks of burrows.

Piddocks

Smooth round holes found in rocks and pebbles have often been created by *Pholadidae* bivalves known commonly as piddocks. One shell has a set of teeth that grind away at clay or rock to produce burrows. The animal will live in the same burrow for its entire lifespan of up to 8 years.

Mammal teeth and bones

The Pleistocene epoch, which began 2.6 million years ago, is very recent in geological terms. This area was overrun by a succession of ice sheets, finally ending when the climate warmed around 11,500 years ago. Most of the glacial deposits in Yorkshire were deposited during the last glaciation. Ice sheets from the North Sea pushed inland leaving thick deposits of boulder clay. But older deposits are occasionally preserved and these can contain mammal remains indicating much warmer conditions.

The cliffs around Boggle Hole and along most of the coast are covered in ice age boulder clay.

Kirkdale Cave

The greatest find of mammal bones in this region was made at Kirkdale cave near Kirkbymoorside in 1831. While quarrying limestone for a nearby road, workers discovered hundreds of old bone fragments. These were identified by the famous geologist William Buckland as belonging to a huge range of animals, including rhinoceros, deer, mammoths and birds. His ground-breaking work established that this was a long-used cave of hyenas, who dragged animal carcasses back to their den before crunching them to pieces.

Buckland's work was the first to establish the behaviour and environment of prehistoric animals, thereby giving impetus to the new science of palaeontology – literally 'the study of ancient life'. We now know that the Kirkdale Cave hyena den existed in the warm interglacial period known as the Ipswichian, around 100,000 years ago.

Rhino and horse teeth and the end of an ox bone from the Kirkdale cave.

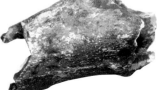

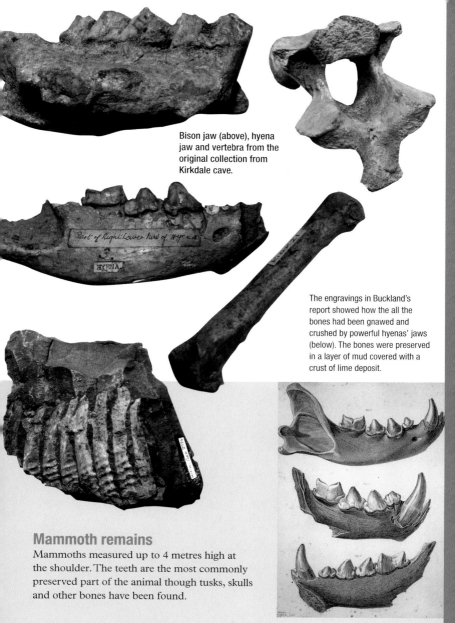

Bison jaw (above), hyena jaw and vertebra from the original collection from Kirkdale cave.

Part of Right Lower Jaw of Hyena

HYÆNA

The engravings in Buckland's report showed how the all the bones had been gnawed and crushed by powerful hyenas' jaws (below). The bones were preserved in a layer of mud covered with a crust of lime deposit.

Mammoth remains

Mammoths measured up to 4 metres high at the shoulder. The teeth are the most commonly preserved part of the animal though tusks, skulls and other bones have been found.

High Tide Books

This pocket book is the latest in our series of guides to the beautiful landscapes of the Yorkshire coast and moors. Check out:

The Dinosaur Coast
Rocks and Landscapes of the North York Moors
Beach Finds on the Yorkshire Coast

On our website (www.hightidepublishing/shop) you will also find books of wider interest, including:

The Floating Egg: Episodes in the Making of Geology
Iron, Steam and Money: The Making of the Industrial Revolution

Acknowledgements

The author and publishers are extremely grateful to Byron Blessed, Robin Knight and Tim Burnhill for their help with this book. Thanks also to Whitby Museum for the use of specimens for photographs. Any errors are the sole responsibility of the author and publisher.

Whitby Museum

Whitby Museum is on the west side of the town set in beautiful Pannett Park. Opening hours are 9:30 to 4:30 every day except Mondays. www.whitbymuseum.org.uk

Whitby Museum catalogue numbers are available for most of the fossil specimens in this book. Please email the publishers for details: hightidepublishing@btinternet.com.

Further Reading

These books are more technical guides to the fossils of Jurassic Yorkshire:

British Mesozoic Fossils, Natural History Museum, revised edition 2013
P Rawson and J Wright, *The Yorkshire Coast*, revised edition 2018